A gift for

_____

From

John & Kathy
Dec
_2010_

Talk to the Tail
'cause the whiskers ain't listenin'!

by Oliver Christianson, a.k.a, Revilo

Editor: Jane-Elyse Pryor and Todd Hafer
Designed by: Dan Horton
Cover design by: Wale' Adeniran
Art Director: Mark Cordes

Printed and bound in China
BOK 2039

For:
Sylvia and Zoë

What other famous cartoonists say about Oliver and his work:

Revilo is one of the legends among cool cartoonists.
His drawings are the inspired ink carvings of a man up to his eyeballs
in talent; his writing belies a psyche on a permanent road trip
with unlimited beer. I dig this guy's work. Piraro

With Revilo, you're in the hands of a master!!!
There's always something profound about his work...This book is
funny in a way that runs deep!! John Callahan

Grrr! Ruff! Ruff! Peep! Peep! Meow! Meow! Bad Kitty! Great
and funny! Benita Epstein

This book is proof that Oliver Christianson should be looked upon
as a moral compass by the citizens of this great nation...
Nay-the world! Randy Rider

I loved Revilo's cartoon book about pets, but my dog was really offended.   Barbara Dale

People tell me Oliver is rude, insulting, and desperate...but to me, he's always been the opposite...desperate, insulting, and rude.
Jeff Keane, Family Circus

Oliver Christianson is to cartooning what Dom DeLuise is to hang gliding...   Steve McGarry, National Cartoonist Society President

Oliver is a lot like pet hair - always sticking to your pants, except you can't lift him off with a lint roller.
Rick Kirkman, Baby Blues

Talk to the Tail

'cause the whiskers ain't listenin'!

SECRET DOGGIE THOUGHTS

"THAT BETTER NOT BE MY WATCH."

Palm Beach resident walking
the world's smallest dog.

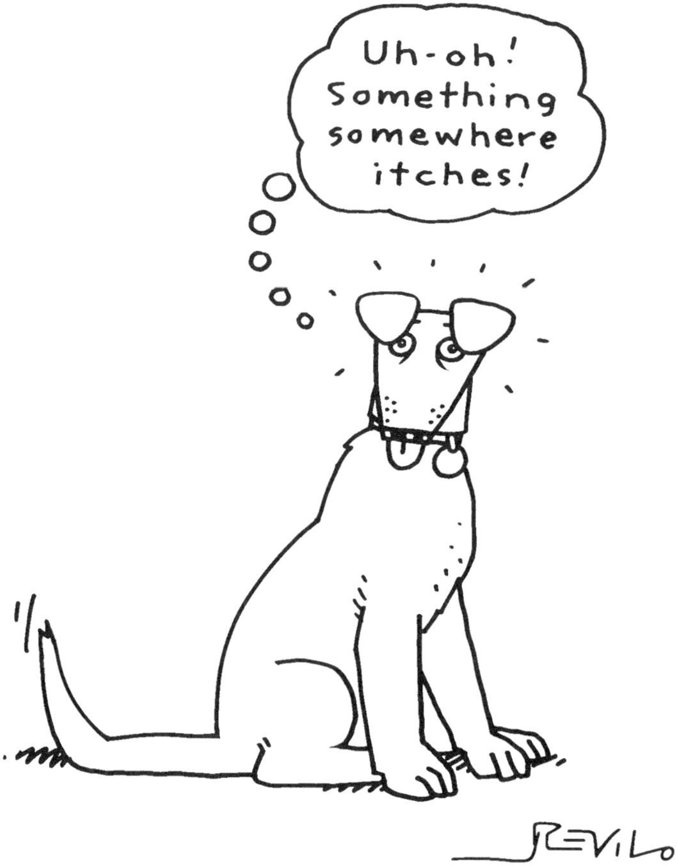
Uh-oh! Something somewhere itches!
REVILO

"DON'T LIE TO ME, YOU'RE DRAGGING YOUR FOOT, I CAN FEEL IT!"

...AND NOW, OUR NATIONAL ANTHEM AS
BARKED BY LASSIE.

Edgar would ultimately regret
taking seduction advice
from his dog, Ranger.

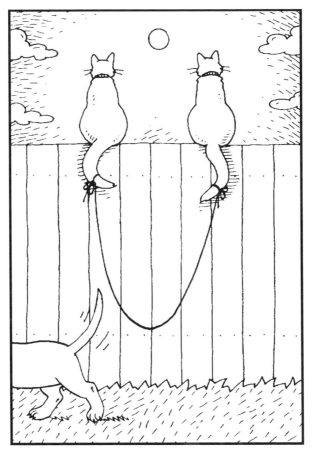

REVILO

PASSING

"In the coming year, I resolve to curb my obsession with parakeets."

" WHAT I HEAR YOU SAYING IS: 'QUACK! QUACK! QUACK!'"

"I THINK YOU KNOW VERY WELL <u>WHO</u>, MR. SCREECH OWL, IF THAT <u>IS</u> YOUR REAL NAME!"

DECORATIVE CAT TAIL COVERS

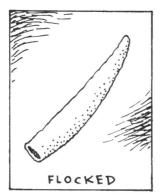

FLOCKED

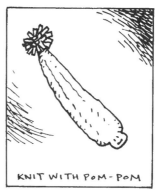

KNIT WITH POM-POM

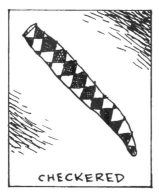

CHECKERED

SHAG

REViLo

So, I'm talking to this really cute guy for like twenty minutes and he's so nice. Well, then we say "good-bye," and as I'm walking away, I catch a glimpse of myself in a store window-- MY LEFT EAR WAS TURNED INSIDE OUT THE WHOLE TIME!!! I could've died! I swear!

I'm an enchanted rodent and if you let me go, I'll tell you where you can find a really long piece of yarn!

A CAT DISGUISED AS A POODLE.

15-POUND CAT IN A
SIZE 5½ SHOE BOX.

Lady →

Her Owner

REVILO

HOW TO TELL THE DIFFERENCE BETWEEN A YOUNG CAT AND AN OLD CAT:

THE FIRST CAT ON THE MOON

I SPEND A LOT OF TIME THINKING
ABOUT YOU.

IT HELPS ME KILL TIME IN BETWEEN
MEALS.

COPYCAT

CAT STAND-UP

SHORTLY BEFORE THE BIG CRASH

LITTLE KNOWN FACTS: A CAT WEIGHS TWICE

AS MUCH WHEN IT IS SLEEPING!

WE COULD CUT OUR HEATING COSTS BY 35%
IF EVERYONE SLEPT IN THEIR DRYER.

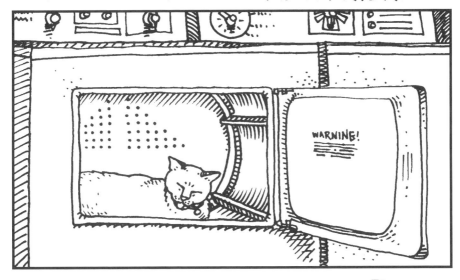

CAT LOVE

A CAT PLANNING OUT
ITS HOLIDAY SCHEDULE

HOW CATS COMMUNICATE:

When Cats Dream. . .

BEING A FIXED MALE HAS ITS MOMENTS...

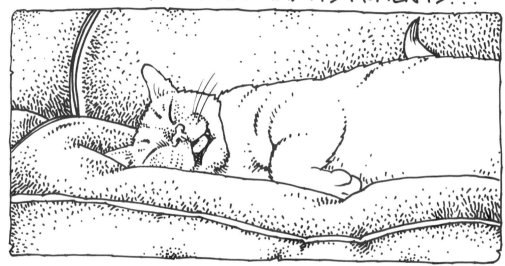

BUT HE MANAGES TO SLEEP THROUGH THEM.

THE MIDNIGHT RIDER

HOW TO PROPERLY FOLD A CAT FOR STORAGE IN A SWEATER DRAWER

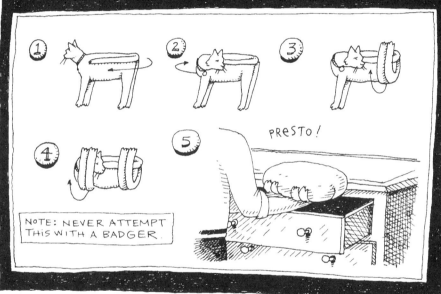

AERIAL VIEW of THE TACKY CAT IN A SHOEBOX

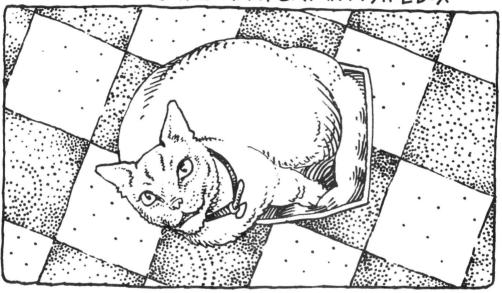

A CAT MAP

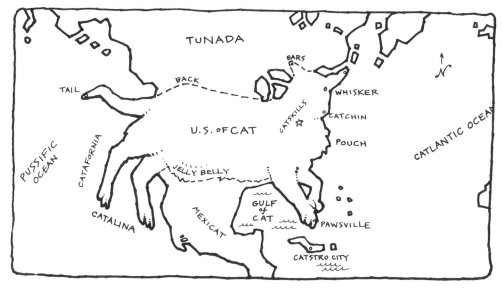

THE TRADITIONAL HOLIDAY DINNER

WITH ALL THE TRIMMINGS (INCLUDING TACKY CAT)

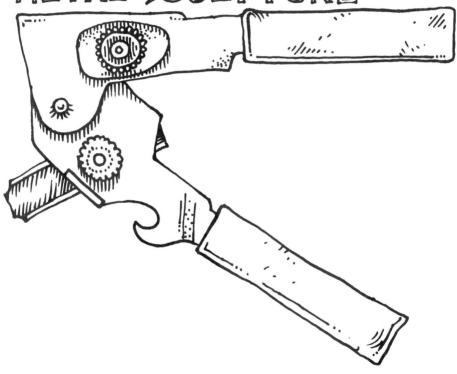

TACKY CAT'S FAVORITE
"METAL SCULPTURE"

THE "STARING AT THE
EMPTY BOWL" TRICK

TACKY CAT INSPECTING SIDEWALK.

THE RETURN of PUSS'N'CLOGS

DIRTY WATER IS ALWAYS MORE TASTY.

TACKY CAT HAVING A RELIGIOUS EXPERIENCE

...IN A NEW OIL SPOT ON THE DRIVEWAY.

CATS ARE TOUGH TO FOOL.

BUD AND DEB MAKE ARMPIT MUSIC
FOR THEIR CAT SYLVIA.

THINGS WE ALL SUSPECT
BUT CAN'T PROVE

Our pets are laughing at us
behind our backs.

If you, or your pet, have enjoyed,
or been offended by, this book,
Hallmark would love to hear from you.
Please send your comments to:
Book Feedback
Hallmark Cards, Inc.
2501 McGee, Mail Drop 489
Kansas City, MO 64141-6580
Or e-mail us at
booknotes@Hallmark.com.